REVIEWS

"Hilarious! An absolute must for every Christmas
"Simply hilarious and entertaining — your kids w
"A laugh-out-loud book"
"Kids will read this clever book again and ag
"My 7-year-old son could not stop laughing

If you enjoyed this book, please kindly leave a rev
on Amazon (left) and Goodreads (right):

Grant S. Clark books

Children's novels
Monkey Magic: The Curse of Mukada
Monkey Magic: The Great Wall Mystery
key Magic: The Ghostly Thieves of New York

Humorous verse for kids
Uncle Bill's Missing Tooth
The Extra Gifted Mr Fripp
The Mystery of Windy Bay

How to Avoid Brussels Sprouts

INSTRUCTIONS FOR A SPROUT-LESS

GRANT S CLARK

ISBN 9781739923358

Contents

Brussels Sprou...
why?

One place I'll gladly never go —
It's known for fries and mussels —
But also has the world's worst food:
The Belgian city, Brussels.

Those Belgians should be filled with sham...
For this, there is no doubt,
Since their true crime against mankind:
Inventing Brussels sprouts.

A vegetable that reeks when boiled
Like fart-and-bad-egg smoothie,
Deserves to join the dinosaurs:
Extinct (except in movies).

JINGLE
MY BRE
SMELLS

Sprouts look so sweet and innocent,
Like cutesy baby cabbage,
But take a crunch, a squelchy munch,
You'd think you're chewing garbage.

Like Sweden gave us swede,
And Chile has its red peppers
That burn you when you feed.

What were the Germans thinking
When they dreamed up sauerkraut?
But those extremes taste like ice cream
Compared with Brussels sprouts!

Once swallowed sprouts are easily
Digested — this is true,
Since stomachs need not do a lot
To turn them into poo.

So what a way on Christmas day
To crush the joy kids feel,
By boiling up a pot of sprouts —
No gift's worth that ordeal.

To end sprout hell at Christmas:
Stick to your plan, this book in hand,
And keep your tummy *sprout-less*.

facts

n boiled for ages, Brussels sprouts go mushy,
tink like rotten eggs and taste revolting.

egetable dictionary says Brussels sprouts are
ll buds of an evil type of cabbage despised by
articularly in households that celebrate Christmas."

It is like
a hot tub

ed sprouts to kids is against the Geneva Convention
n the Rights of the Child (or soon will be).

loving doctors claim Brussels sprouts are good for you
ause they contain lots of vitamins and fibre.

nd that sprouts are the least favourite Christmas veg —
f 10 adults dislike them. For kids, it is 10 out of 10.

is said to have been "sprouted."

A Swedish man called Linus holds the world record
the most sprouts in one minute: 31 sprout

A British Royal Navy commanding officer bar
sprouts from his ship because he hated them so
and worried (rightly) that they'd stink the boat

* When love breaks down, they become "prefab sprouts"

The accepted term for lots of sprouts is a "nightmare of sprouts."

"A nightmare of sprouts"

record for the heaviest sprout is 8.3 kilograms (18 pounds). 's the weight of three bricks or three small cats.

or perish!
I guess we surrender
'We said surrender or perish, you idiots!'
I have an idea
'WE SURRENDER!!'
Ugh the smell!
OVER & SPROUT

How to Avoid
russels Sprouts

Flick them out the window,
Sneak them in the trash,
Hide them in the wrapping paper,
Shove them in the mash.

"FLICK THEM OUT
THE WINDOW"

Everybody join in!

YOU-CAN-DO-32

YOU-CAN-DO 32

'Til your plate is full of leaves,
Send them flying everywhere
With one almighty sneeze.

ACHOO!

Drop a sprout upon your knee
Then roll it good and slow,
Bend the sprout like Beckham
So it flies out the window.

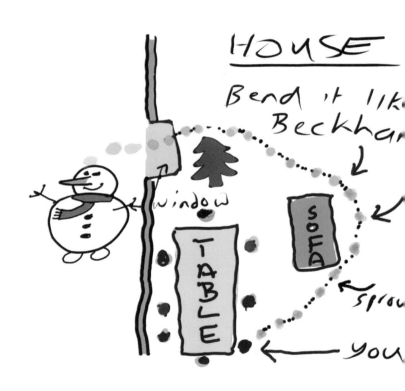

Loosen up some baubles
Hanging from the Christmas tree,
Squeeze some soggy sprouts inside —
And hope that no one sees.

Beneath her Christmas log,
Store a sprout inside each cheek
Then spit them down the bog.

Dress the dogs like aliens,
A note upon their snouts:
"Our planet soon will perish
If we don't take all your sprouts."

Grab one tight and stretch up high
(Ignore the squishy feeling),
Launch the sprout with all your might
So it sticks to the ceiling.

Begin to sing and shout,
Tell Dad it's his Christmas gift:
A thousand-gig I-sprout.

Squish one in your back pocket
Or between Grandpa's toes,
If the sprouts are small enough
Then stuff one up your nose.

'Nose' sign of sprouts

Make a fake by mashing up
A ball of peas and stuffing,
Scoff it down — you're done with sprouts!
(Unless they see you're bluffing.)

And plant one in the ground —
A risky move as soon enough
You'll grow a sprouty mound.

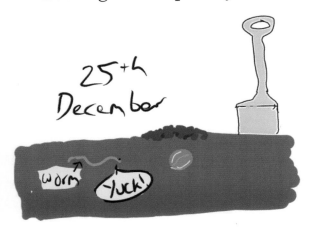

Cry out: "I'm with Greta!"
Warn the adults of the danger:
The clouds of fart from eating sprouts
Make us all climate-changers.

To make sprouts disappear,
If your lugs are big enough
Stick one behind each ear.

"Goodness, Emily! You ate your sprouts! Where did they all go?"

They are behind ear"

Stick some string onto a sprout
To make a wee "sprout mouse,"
Drop it when the cat is near —
She'll chase it round the house.

A golden rule to keep things cool:
The young must stick together.
Do not dump sprouts on fellow kids
Unless it is your brother!

Add a message for good cheer:
"This is what a giant gets
When he cleans out his ear."

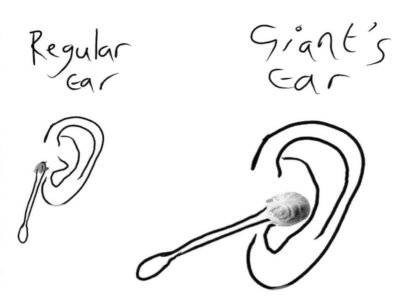

Regular
ear

Giant's
ear

Hide one in a potato
You've neatly hollowed out,
Say you don't have room for it —
"At least I ate my sprout!"

Take a course in flicking
Practice hard until it's easy —
Place a sprout upon your thumb
And land it in your hoodie.

squidge some sp...uts together,
From the garden you can call:
"Come and kick my eco-friendly,
   Stinky green sprout-ball."

Get up early — find the veg
And throw those stink bombs out,
Tell your folks that burglars struck
   But only took the sprouts!

Which you must go back to clear,
Or Santa will get stuck in guck
From mouldy sprouts next year.

Now, if somehow these methods fail
And they're still on your plate,
Drown your sprouts in ketchup
And resign yourself to fate...

Like all bad things, this too shall pass —
You'll soon eat tasty grub —
Be proud that you're a member of
The sprout survivors' club!

This secret document, found in the vaults of Secret Belgian Vegetable Museum, reveals how Brus were invented (translations on the right).

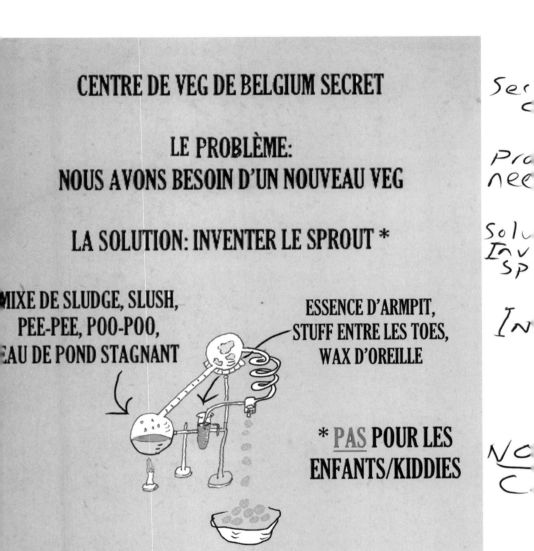

CENTRE DE VEG DE BELGIUM SECRET

LE PROBLÈME:
NOUS AVONS BESOIN D'UN NOUVEAU VEG

LA SOLUTION: INVENTER LE SPROUT *

MIXE DE SLUDGE, SLUSH,
PEE-PEE, POO-POO,
EAU DE POND STAGNANT

ESSENCE D'ARMPIT,
STUFF ENTRE LES TOES,
WAX D'OREILLE

* PAS POUR LES
ENFANTS/KIDDIES

Se
c

Pro
nee

Solu
Inv
SP

In

Nc
C

Discovery

Since writing these instructions
A discovery was made:
Some kind and clever chefs tried cooking
Sprouts in different ways.

Instead of over-boiling sprouts
To terrorise our guts,
They roasted them and fried them up
With garlic, spice and nuts.

It's hard to write without some fright
(Those things still haunt my tummy),
But cooked all good and crispy
Sprouts are actually quite yummy.

"A sprout's nightmare"

When it comes to Brussels, too:
A great city that's fun to see
(With boiled sprouts off menus).

A final tip: Be careful
How you word your Christmas list.
I asked that I should *see no sprouts*,
Mum then produced a dish...

A crust of chilli swede on top,
Then globs of sauerkraut,
And hidden at the bottom:
A nightmare of Brussels sprouts!

The worst dish ever

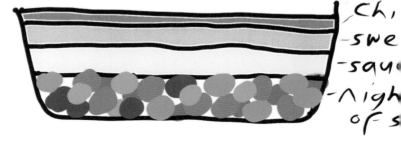

Ch,
-swe
-squ
-Nigh
of s

d vegetable is by far the most disgusting in the world?

/hich vegetable rhymes with *muscles trouts*?

. Which small and round veg, when boiled,
    stinks the home out for ages?

table can be formed from the letters: *burps tosses slur*?

/hich vegetable is the subject of a book called
    How to Avoid Brussels Sprouts?

an called Linus ate 31 of which vegetable in one minute?

rd veg weighed the same as three bricks or small cats?

getable has the scientific name *Solanum tuberosum*?

when I grow
up I want
to be a
cabbage!

FOOD ALLERGY

I am allergic to sprouts
I cannot eat Brussels sprouts,
even small ones. They turn
me into a very angry person.
I or others near me may
require medical attention.
Sprouts can be found in:
* Boiled sprouts
* Christmas dinner or lunch
* Sprout omelette
* Sticky sprout pudding
Does this meal contain sprouts?

Attention! Medics re
keeping sprouts out
house. It is fine to re
them with peas or ch
Thank you!

Answers

1. Brussels sprouts

2. Brussels sprouts

3. Brussels sprouts

4. Brussels sprouts

5. Brussels sprouts

6. Brussels sprouts

7. Brussels sprouts

8. Potato

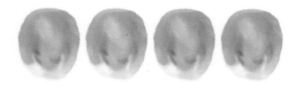

"One of the best Christmas books you will buy. '
laugh out loud book by one of my son's favourite
Full of funny Christmas poetry that would bring
onto any child's face." Thea (Goodreads revi

"An excellent, witty book suitable for ages up tc
Very funny, quite informative if you want it t
and great illustrations." Rob (Amazon revie

"Farts and laughs — an absolute treat of a book. And
assured... sprouts may be the butt of every joke, but
ultimately one of redemption both for the pongy bal
and for Christmas lunch." Eli (Amazon revie

"My daughters and I loved this book. You might love or h
one thing I know is that you will love this book. It's simp
entertaining — your kids will love it." Lisa (Amazon revi

"An amusing poetry book with useful tips on how you
sprouts at Christmas. Children of all ages will love this.
son could not stop laughing." Joao (Amazon re

"Kids will read this clever book again and again. *How to*
Sprouts is joining our shelf of holiday classics, along w
Night and *The 12 Dogs of Christmas*. There's a laugh or
this whimsical book about the dread kids feel when t
universally-loathed vegetable on their plates." Virgin

you liked *How to Avoid Brussels Sprouts,*

e *Uncle Bill's Missing Tooth,* another Grant S. Clark

– illustrated by the brilliant Lizzie Nelson. And look out

coming releases: *The Extra-Gifted Mr Fripp* and

The Mystery of Stinker Bay.

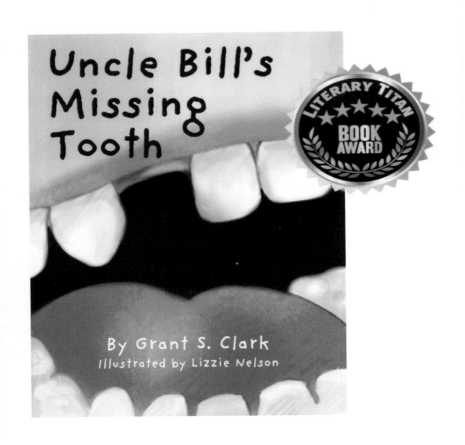

E FOR UNCLE BILL'S MISSING TOOTH

y good book that will keep the children entertained."
RUGBY LEGEND SIR BILL BEAUMONT

k! We have really enjoyed reading it!" **TANA RAMSAY**

iggle a verse!" **STRAWBERRY SUMMERTIME REVIEWS**

..entertaining from cover to cover." **LITERARY TITAN**

has worked as a jour
and Asia as well as w
books. He is the auth
Monkey Magic seri
Alexander adventure
sprouts when they ar
loves them cooked otl
out more at grantscla

PRAISE FOR MONKEY MAGIC

"A beautifully written tale of good vs evil that will insp:
NATIONAL GEOGRAPHIC KIDS
"Cleverly woven with delicious subplots."
KIDS BOOK REVIEW

"A gripping adventure with an important messa
JEREMY STRONG, AUTHOR
"A super book! Please buy it, treasure it and share its
DAVID BELLAMY, CONSERVATION LEGE
"A fantastic novel!" **THE MIDWEST BOOK REV**

The Curse of Mukada was nominated for the
Hedwig Anuar children's book of the year.

Printed in Great Britain
by Amazon

52813147R00018